EASIEST KEYBOARD COLLECTION

80s Hits

WISE PUBLICATIONS
London/New York/Paris/Sydney/Copenhagen/Madrid

Exclusive Distributors:

Music Sales Limited
8/9 Frith Street,
London W1V 5TZ, England.

Music Sales Pty Limited
120 Rothschild Avenue,
Rosebery, NSW 2018,
Australia.

Order No. AM955779
ISBN 0-7119-7409-8
This book © Copyright 1999 by Wise Publications

Book design by Chloë Alexander
Compiled by Peter Evans
Music arranged by Roger Day
Music processed by Paul Ewers Music Design

Printed in the United Kingdom by
Caligraving Limited, Thetford, Norfolk.

Cover photograph courtesy of The Image Bank

Your Guarantee of Quality
As publishers, we strive to produce every book to the highest
commercial standards.
The music has been freshly engraved and the book has been carefully
designed to minimise awkward page turns and to make playing from
it a real pleasure.
Particular care has been given to specifying acid-free, neutral-sized
paper made from pulps which have not been elemental chlorine
bleached. This pulp is from farmed sustainable forests and was
produced with special regard for the environment.
Throughout, the printing and binding have been planned to ensure
a sturdy, attractive publication which should give years of enjoyment.
If your copy fails to meet our high standards, please inform us and
we will gladly replace it.

Music Sales' complete catalogue describes thousands of titles and is
available in full colour sections by subject, direct from Music Sales
Limited. Please state your areas of interest and send a cheque/postal
order for £1.50 for postage to: Music Sales Limited, Newmarket Road,
Bury St. Edmunds, Suffolk IP33 3YB.

Contents

A WOMAN IN LOVE

Words & Music by Barry Gibb & Robin Gibb

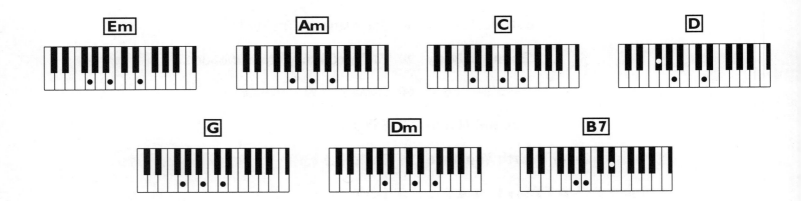

Voice: **Piano 2**

Rhythm: **Pop Ballad**

Tempo: ♩ = 100

Life is a mo-ment in space, when the dream is gone,— it's a lone-li-er place,

I kiss the morn-ing good-bye,— but down in-side

—— you know we nev-er know why.—— The road is nar-row and long——

—— when eyes meet eyes—— and the feel-ing is strong.——

I turn a-way from the wall,___ I stum-ble and fall,___ but I give you it all.___

I am a wo-man in love___ and I'd do a-ny-thing___ to get you in-to my world,

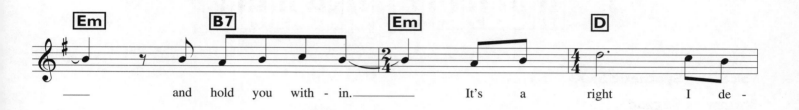

___ and hold you with - in._____ It's a right I de-

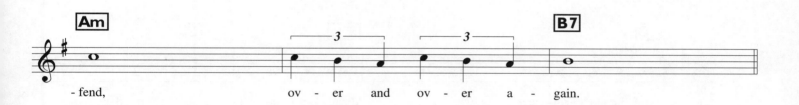

- fend, ov - er and ov - er a - gain.

I am a wo-man in love___ and I'd do a-ny-thing___ to get you in-to my world

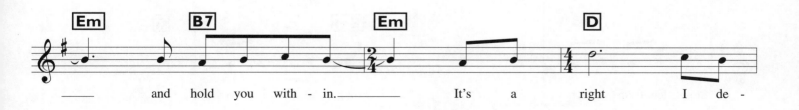

___ and hold you with - in._____ It's a right I de-

Repeat ad lib.

- fend ov - er and ov - er a - gain.

BUFFALO SOLDIER

Words & Music by Bob Marley & Noel Williams

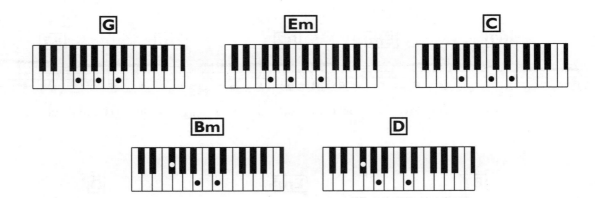

Voice: **Synthetic SFX**

Rhythm: **Reggae**

Tempo: ♩= 130

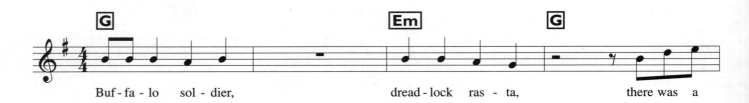

Buf - fa - lo sol - dier,   dread - lock ras - ta,   there was a

buf - fa - lo sol - dier   in the heart of A - me - ri - ca.

Sto - len from A - fri - ca,   brought to A - me - ri - ca,

fight - ing on ar - ri - val,   fight - ing for sur - vi - val.   I mean it.

EBONY AND IVORY

Words & Music by McCartney

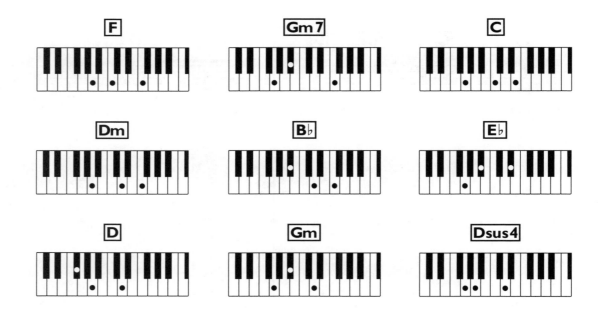

Voice: **Strings/Piano**

Rhythm: **8 Beat Pop**

Tempo: ♩ = 98

E - bo - ny___ and i - vo - ry___ live to - geth - er in per - fect

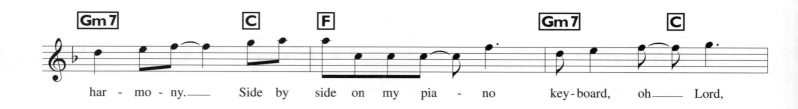

har - mo - ny.___ Side by side on my pia - no key-board, oh___ Lord,

why don't we?___

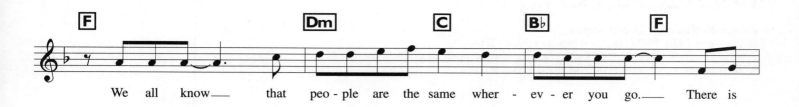

We all know—— that peo - ple are the same wher - ev - er you go.—— There is

good and bad in ev - 'ry - one, we learn to live, we

learn to give each oth - er what we need to sur - vive,—— to - geth - er a - live.——

E - bo - ny—— and i - vo - ry—— live to - geth - er in per - fect

har - mo - ny.—— Side by side on my pia - no key - board, oh—— Lord,

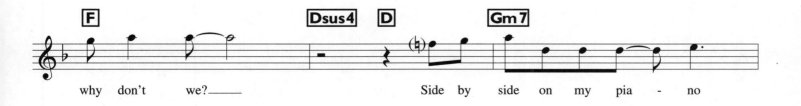

why don't we?—— Side by side on my pia - no

key - board, oh—— Lord why don't we?——

ENDLESS LOVE

Words & Music by Lionel Richie
© Copyright 1981 PGP Music & Brockman Music, USA.
Warner Chappell Music Limited, Griffin House, 161 Hammersmith Road, London W6.
All Rights Reserved. International Copyright Secured.

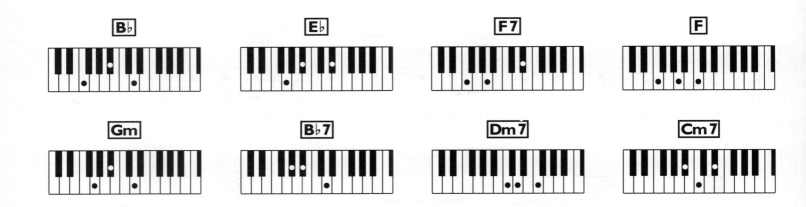

Voice: **Brass Ensemble**

Rhythm: **Soul Ballad**

Tempo: ♩= 106

My love,—— there's on-ly you in my life,——

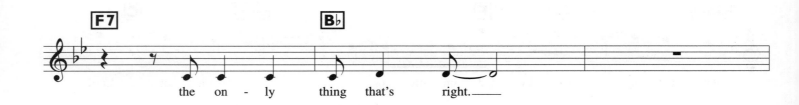

the on-ly thing that's right.——

My first love,—— you're ev-'ry breath that I take,——

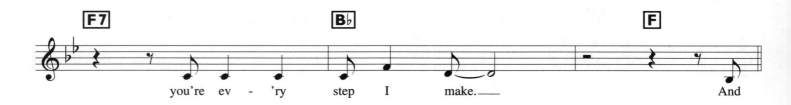

you're ev-'ry step I make.—— And

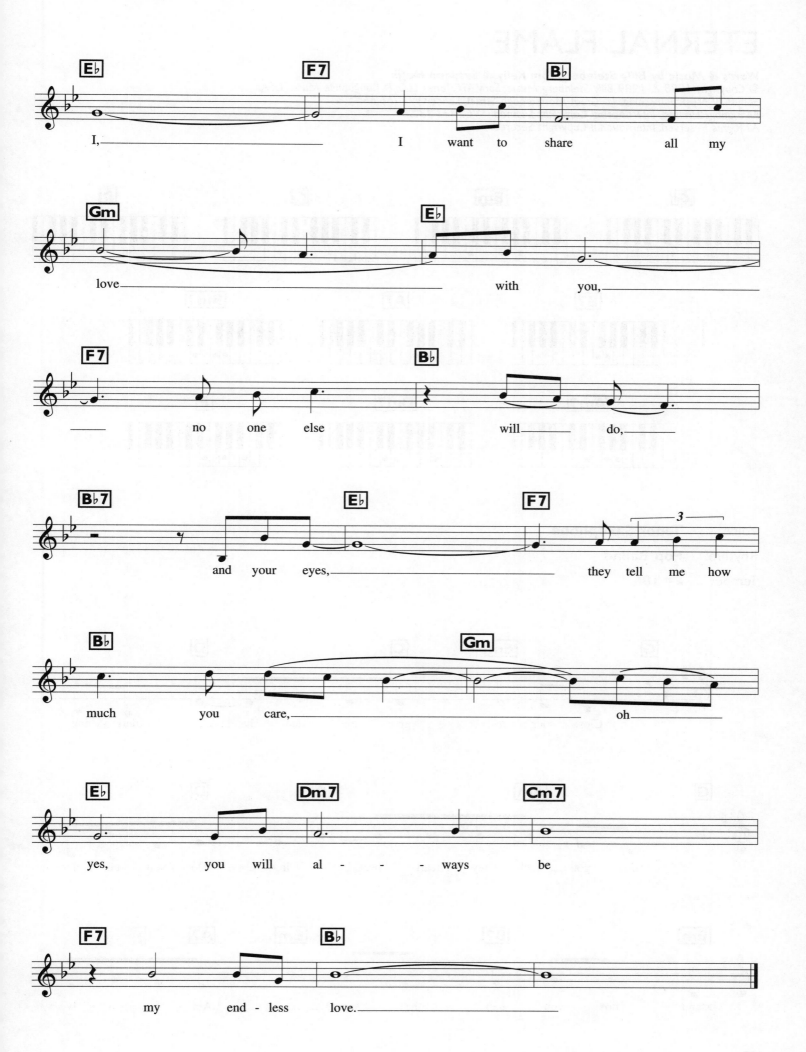

ETERNAL FLAME

Words & Music by Billy Steinberg, Tom Kelly & Susanna Hoffs

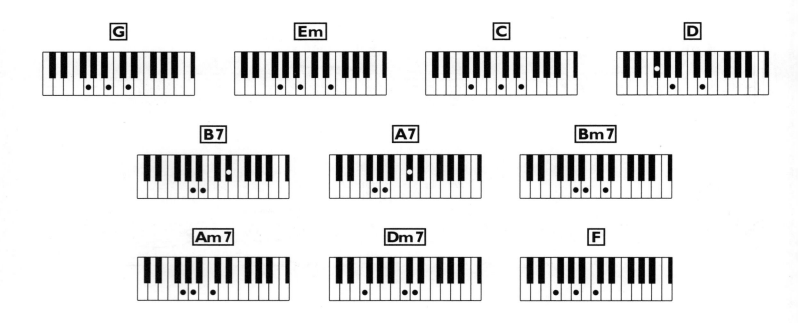

Voice: **Tenor Saxophone**

Rhythm: **Pop Ballad**

Tempo: ♩ = 106

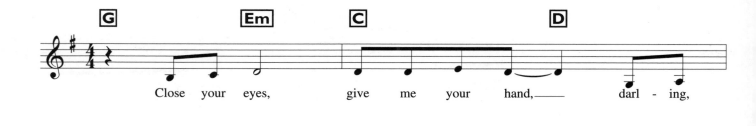

Close your eyes, give me your hand,___ darl - ing,

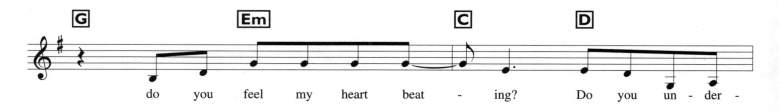

do you feel my heart beat - ing? Do you un - der -

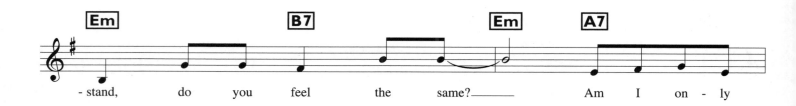

- stand, do you feel the same?___ Am I on - ly

dream - ing? Is this burn - ing an e - ter - nal flame?

Say my name, sun shines through the rain,_____ a whole

life so lone - ly and then come and ease the pain._____

I don't wan - na lose this feel - ing, oh.

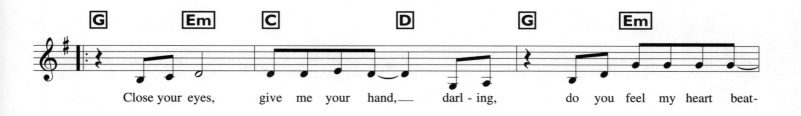

Close your eyes, give me your hand,___ darl - ing, do you feel my heart beat-

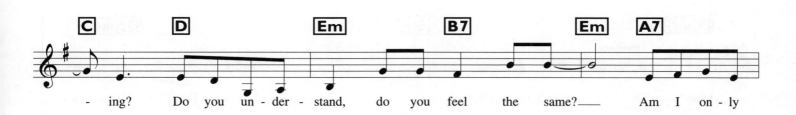

- ing? Do you un - der - stand, do you feel the same?___ Am I on - ly

Repeat to fade

dream - ing? Is this burn - ing an e - ter - nal flame?

EVERY BREATH YOU TAKE

Words & Music by Sting
© Copyright 1983 G.M. Sumner.
EMI Music Publishing Limited/Magnetic Publishing Limited.
All Rights Reserved. International Copyright Secured.

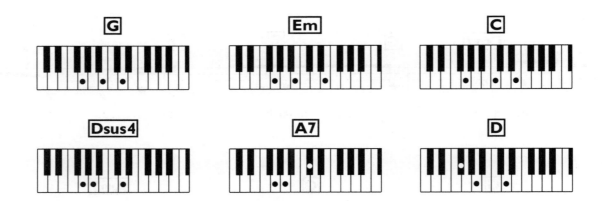

Voice: **Electric Piano 2**

Rhythm: **16 Beat Funky**

Tempo: ♩ = 118

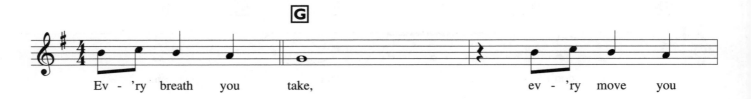

Ev - 'ry breath you take, ev - 'ry move you

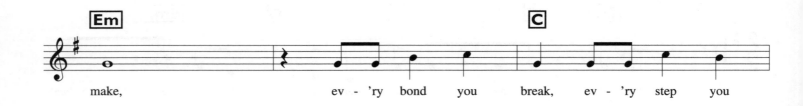

make, ev - 'ry bond you break, ev - 'ry step you

take, I'll be watch - ing you. Ev - 'ry sin - gle

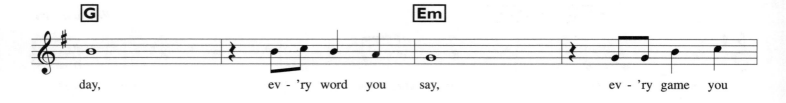

day, ev - 'ry word you say, ev - 'ry game you

play, ev - 'ry night you stay, I'll be watch-ing you.   Oh can't you

see   you be - long to me?   How my poor heart

aches_____ with ev - 'ry breath you take.   Ev - 'ry move you

make,   ev - 'ry vow you break,   Ev - 'ry move you

ev - 'ry smile you fake, ev - 'ry claim you stake, I'll be watch - ing you.

I'll be watch - ing   you._____

I JUST CALLED TO SAY I LOVE YOU

Words & Music by Stevie Wonder
© Copyright 1984 Jobete Music Company Incorporated and Black Bull Music, USA.
Jobete Music (UK) Limited/Black Bull Music, London WC2 for the UK and Eire.
All Rights Reserved. International Copyright Secured.

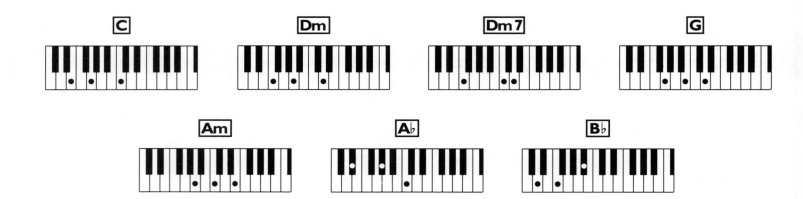

Voice: **Clavelectro**

Rhythm: **Soul Ballad**

Tempo: ♩ = 126

No New Year's Day_____ to ce - le - brate._____

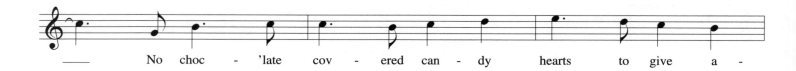

_____ No choc - 'late cov - ered can - dy hearts to give a -

- way._____ No first of Spring,_____

_____ no song to sing,_____ in fact here's

I THINK WE'RE ALONE NOW

Words & Music by Ritchie Cordell

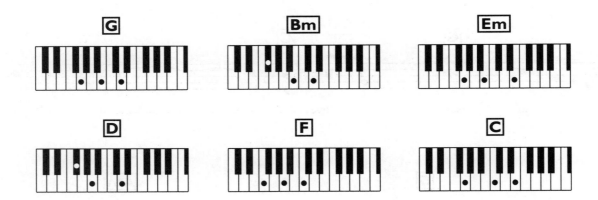

Voice: **Choir/Electric Piano**

Rhythm: **Pop Rock 1**

Tempo: ♩ = 112

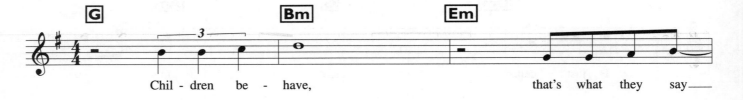

Chil - dren be - have, that's what they say __ when we're to - geth - er,

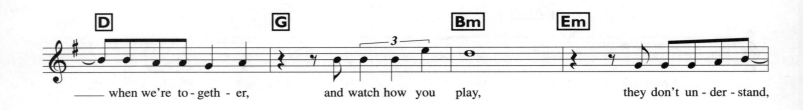

and watch how you play, they don't un - der - stand,

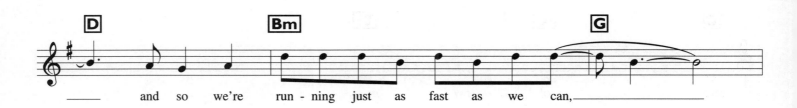

__ and so we're run - ning just as fast as we can, __

hold - ing on to one an - oth - er's hand. __ Try - ing to get __ a - way

LIVIN' ON A PRAYER

Words & Music by Jon Bon Jovi, Richie Sambora & Desmond Child

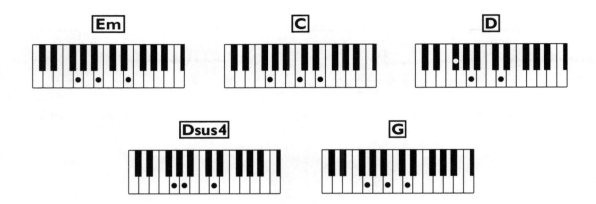

Voice: **Studio Piano**

Rhythm: **Rock**

Tempo: ♩= 120

Tom - my used to work on the docks,_____ u - nion's been on strike, he's

down on his luck, it's tough,_____ so tough._____

_____ Gi - na works the din - er all day,_____

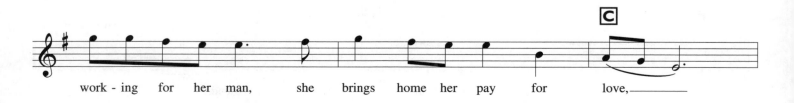

work - ing for her man, she brings home her pay for love,_____

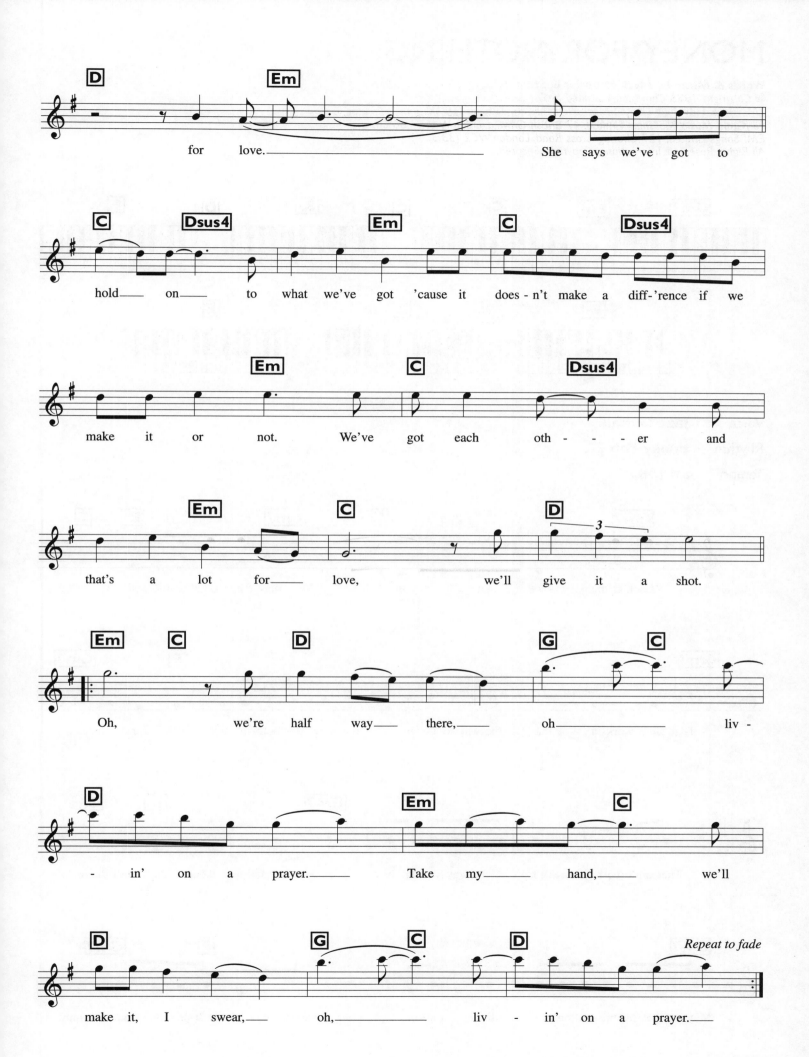

MONEY FOR NOTHING

Words & Music by Mark Knopfler & Sting
© Copyright 1985 Chariscourt Limited (90%) &
EMI Music Publishing Limited/Magnetic Publishing Limited (10%).
All Rights Reserved. International Copyright Secured.

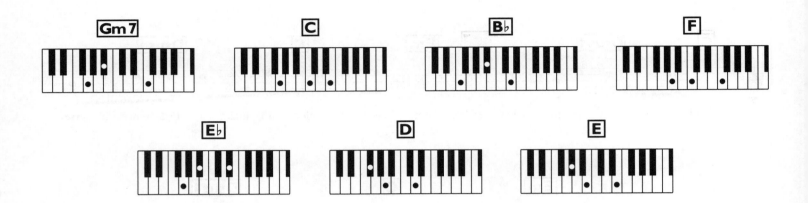

Voice: **Jazz Guitar**

Rhythm: **Funky Pop 2**

Tempo: ♩= 108

Look at them yo-yos, that's— the way to do it, play the gui-tar on the M. T. V.

That ain't work-in', that's— the way to do it, mo-ney for noth-in' and chicks for free—

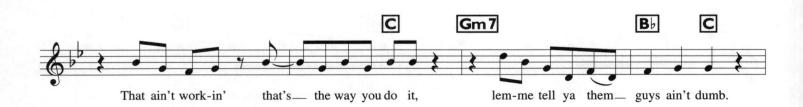

That ain't work-in' that's— the way you do it, lem-me tell ya them— guys ain't dumb.

May-be get a blis-ter on your lit-tle fing-er, may-be get a blist-er on your— thumb.

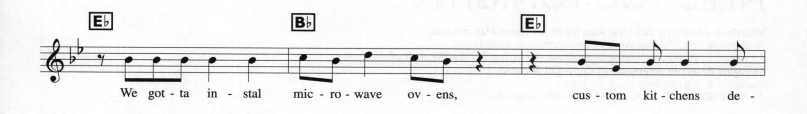

We got-ta in-stal mic-ro-wave ov-ens, cus-tom kit-chens de-

-liv-er-ies.___ We got-ta move these re-fri-ge-ra-tors,

we got-ta move these co-lour T. V.s.___

Look at them yo-yos, that's__ the way to do it, play the gui-tar on the M. T. V.

That ain't work-in', that's__ the way to do it, mo-ney for no-thin' and chicks for free.__

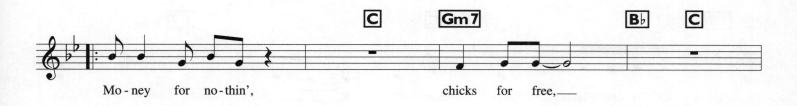

Mo-ney for no-thin', chicks for free,___

Repeat to fade

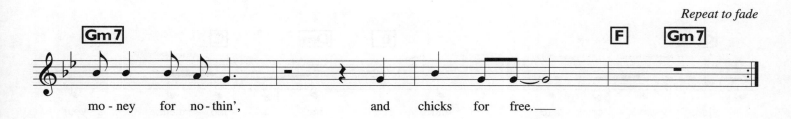

mo-ney for no-thin', and chicks for free.__

NEED YOU TONIGHT

Words & Music by Andrew Farriss & Michael Hutchence
© Copyright 1987 MMA Music International for Australasia.
Published by PolyGram International Music Publishing B.V. for the Rest of the World.
PolyGram Music Publishing Limited, 47 British Grove, London W4.
Published by ToyBox Publishing for Japan.
All Rights Reserved. International Copyright Secured.

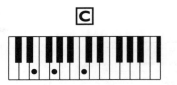

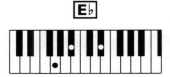
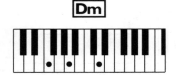

Voice: **Electric Guitar**

Rhythm: **Funky Pop 2**

Tempo: ♩ = 104

All you got is this mo -

- ment,—   the twen - ty first cen - tury's yes - ter - day.

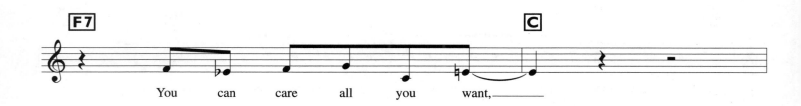

You can care all you want,——

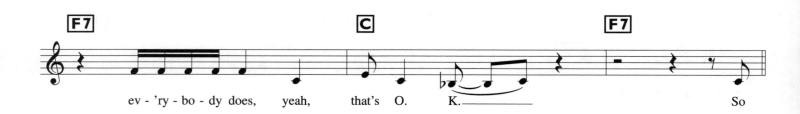

ev - 'ry - bo - dy does, yeah, that's O. K.——   So

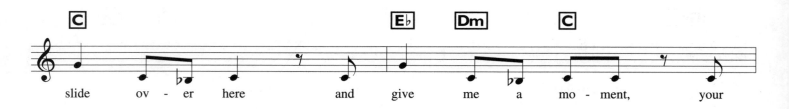

slide ov - er here and give me a mo - ment, your

ON MY OWN

Words & Music by Carole Bayer Sager & Burt Bacharach

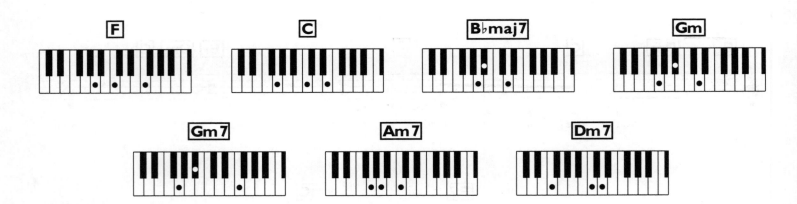

Voice: **Alto Saxophone**

Rhythm: **Soul Ballad**

Tempo: ♩ = 104

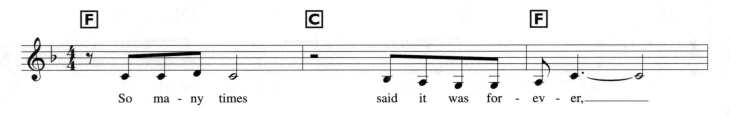

So ma-ny times said it was for-ev-er,____

said our love would al-ways be true.____

Some-thing in my heart al-ways knew I'd be

ly-ing here be-side you.____ On my

PRIVATE DANCER

Words & Music by Mark Knopfler
© Copyright 1984 Straitjacket Songs Limited.
All Rights Reserved. International Copyright Secured.

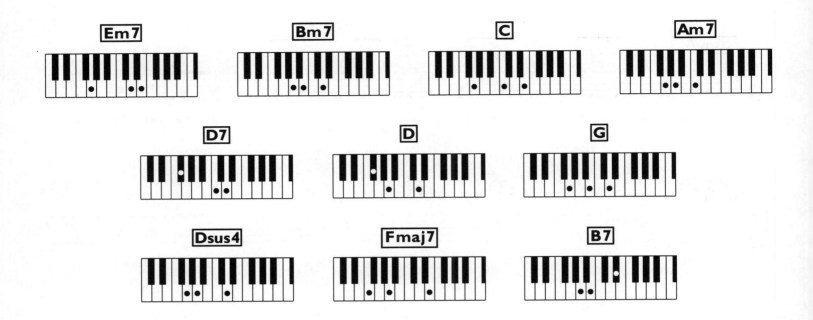

Voice: **Electric Piano 2**

Rhythm: **Pop Rock 1**

Tempo: ♩ = 108

Well the men come in these pla - ces____

and the men are all the same.____ You don't look at their

fac - es____ and you don't ask their name.____

You don't think of them as hu - man, you don't think of them at all. You keep your mind on the

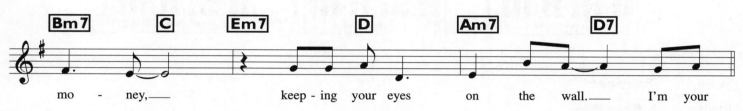

mo - ney, keep - ing your eyes on the wall. I'm your

pri - vate danc - er, a danc - er for mo - ney, I'll

do what you want me to do. I'm your

pri - vate dan - cer, a dan - cer for mo - ney and

Repeat to fade

a - ny old mus - ic will do. I'm your

RIO

Words & Music by Duran Duran

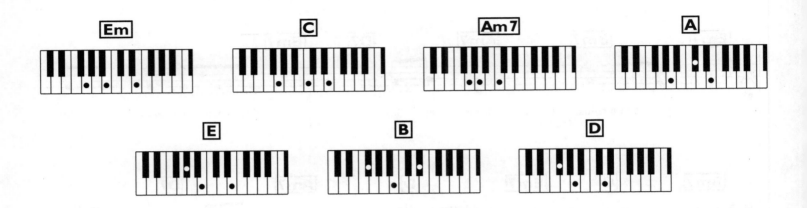

Voice: **Trumpet**

Rhythm: **8 Beat Pop**

Tempo: ♩ = 136

Mov-ing on the floor now babe, you're a bird of pa - ra - dise,

cher - ry ice cream smile, I sup - pose it's ve - ry nice. With a

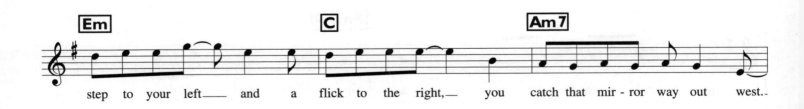

step to your left and a flick to the right, you catch that mir - ror way out west..

You know you're some - thing spe - cial and you

SOMETIMES

Words & Music by Vince Clarke & Andy Bell
© Copyright 1986 Musical Moments Limited/Minotaur Music Limited/
Sony/ATV Music Publishing, 10 Great Marlborough Street, London W1.
All Rights Reserved. International Copyright Secured.

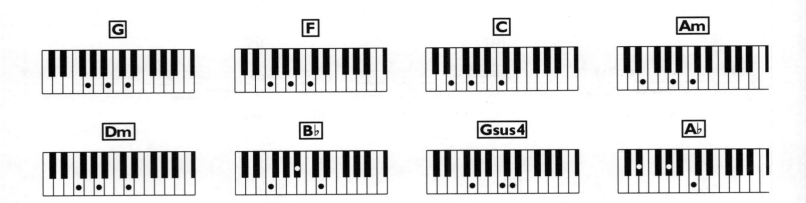

Voice: **Violin**

Rhythm: **Lite Pop**

Tempo: ♩ = **100**

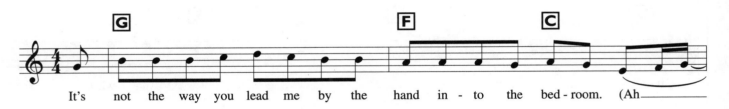

It's not the way you lead me by the hand in-to the bed-room. (Ah_____

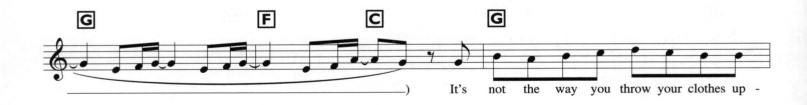

_____) It's not the way you throw your clothes up-

-on the bath-room floor. (Ah_____

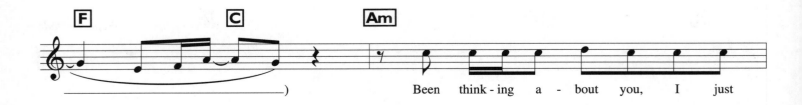

_____) Been think-ing a-bout you, I just

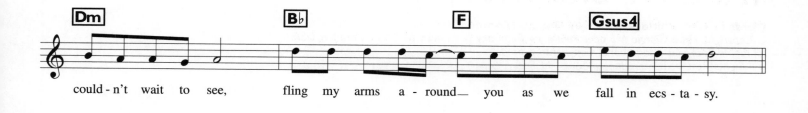

could-n't wait to see, fling my arms a-round you as we fall in ec-ta-sy.

Ooh___ some - times,___ the truth is hard-er than the pain in - side,___

___ yeah.___ Ooh___ some -

- times,___ it's the bro-ken heart that de - cides.___

Ooh___ some - times,___ the truth is hard-er than the pain in - side,___

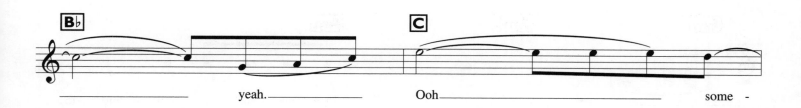

___ yeah.___ Ooh___ some -

Repeat to fade

- times,___ it's the brok-en heart that de - cides.___

TAKE MY BREATH AWAY

Words by Tom Whitlock. Music by Giorgio Moroder

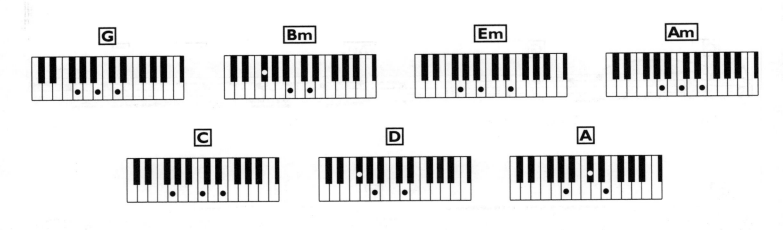

Voice: **Distortion Guitar**

Rhythm: **Soul Ballad**

Tempo: ♩ = 102

Watch-ing ev-'ry mo-tion in_____ my fool-ish lov-er's game,_____

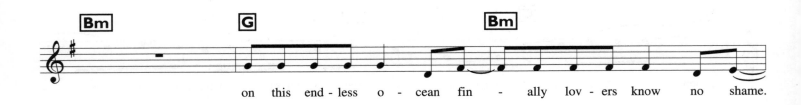

on this end-less o-cean fin - ally lov-ers know no shame.

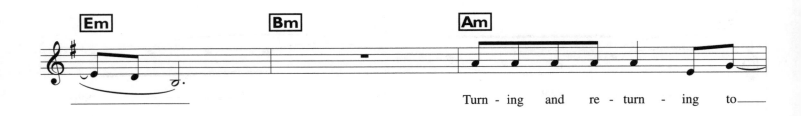

_____ Turn-ing and re-turn-ing to_____

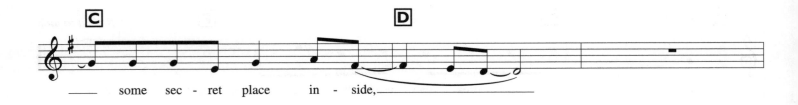

_____ some sec-ret place in-side,_____

watch-ing in slow mo - tion as___ you turn a-round and say,___ take my breath a -

- way.

Through the hour - glass I saw___ you,___ in time you slipped___ a - way.___

___ When the mir - ror crashed I called___ you___ and

turned to hear___ you say "If on - ly for to - day___

___ I___ am un - a - fraid,___ take my breath a -

Repeat to fade

- way." "Take my breath a -

35

THANK YOU FOR THE MUSIC

Words & Music by Benny Andersson & Bjorn Ulvaeus
© Copyright 1977 for the world by Union Songs AB, Sweden.
Bocu Music Limited, 1 Wyndham Yard, Wyndham Place, London W1 for Great Britain and Eire.
All Rights Reserved. International Copyright Secured.

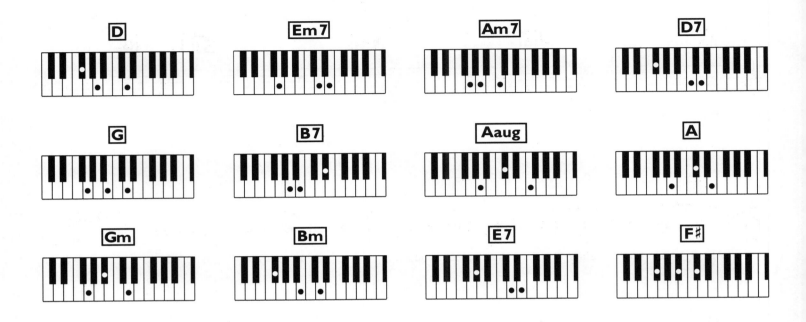

Voice: **Flute**
Rhythm: **Epic Ballad**
Tempo: ♩ = 104

I'm no-thing spe-cial, in fact I'm a bit___ of a bore,___

if I tell a joke___ you've prob-a-bly heard___ it be-fore.

___ But I have a ta-lent, a won-der-ful thing___ 'cause

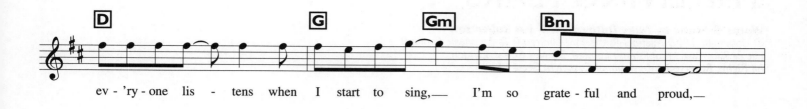

ev-'ry-one lis - tens when I start to sing,— I'm so grate-ful and proud,—

all I want— is to sing— it out loud.— So I say

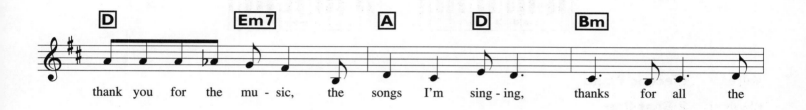

thank you for the mu - sic, the songs I'm sing - ing, thanks for all the

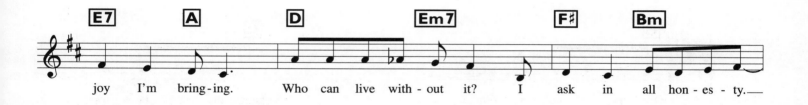

joy I'm bring-ing. Who can live with-out it? I ask in all hon-es-ty.—

—— What would life be,— with-out a song— or dance— what are

we? So I say thank you for the mu-sic, for giv - ing it to me.—

So I say thank you for the mu-sic, for giv - ing it to me.

THE LIVING YEARS

Words & Music by Mike Rutherford & BA Robertson

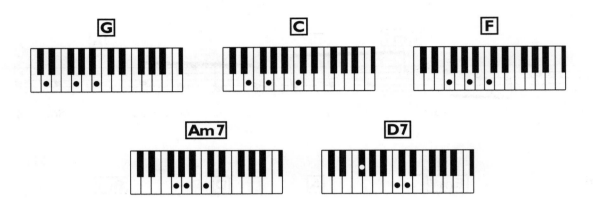

Voice: **Electric Piano**

Rhythm: **8 Beat Pop**

Tempo: ♩ = 112

Ev-'ry ge-ne-ra-tion _____ blames the one be-fore, _____

_____ and all of their frus-tra-tions _____ come

beat-ing on your door. _____ I know that I'm a pris-'ner to all my

fath-er held so dear, I know that I'm a hos-tage to

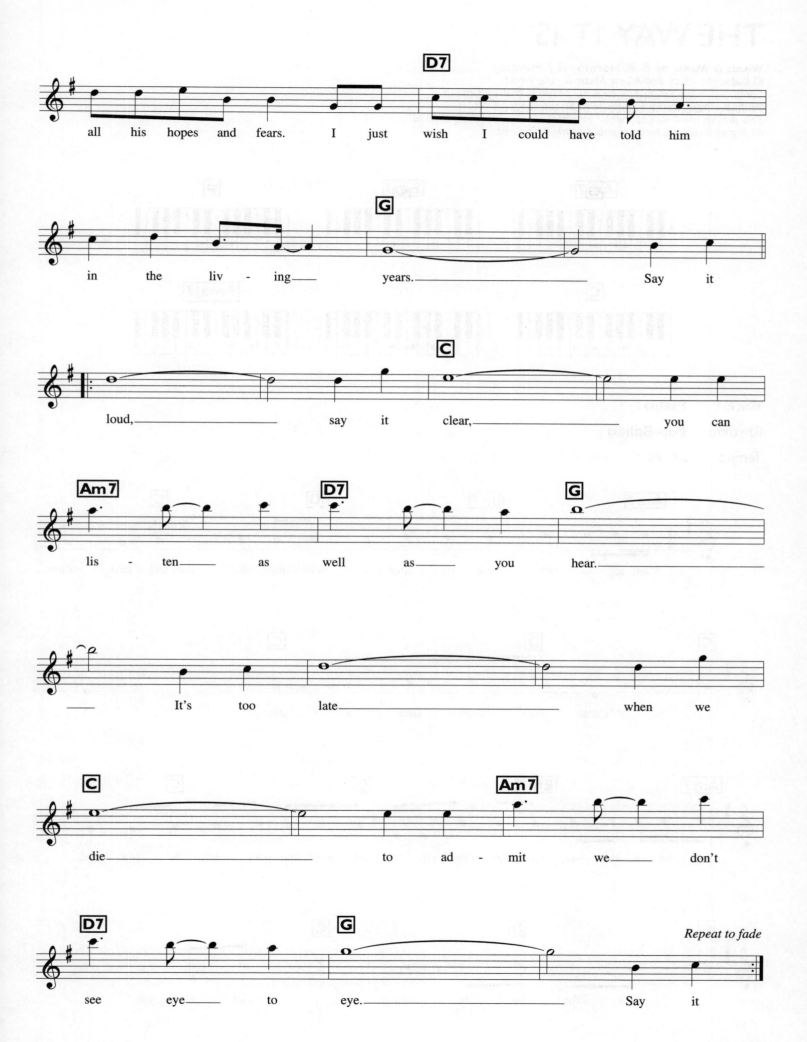

all his hopes and fears. I just wish I could have told him

in the liv - ing years. Say it

loud, say it clear, you can

lis - ten as well as you hear. It's too late

when we die to ad - mit we don't

Repeat to fade

see eye to eye. Say it

THE WAY IT IS

Words & Music by B. R. Hornsby & J. Hornsby

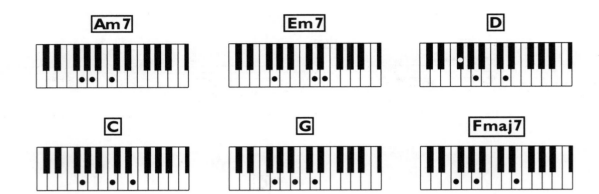

Voice: **Piano**

Rhythm: **Pop Ballad**

Tempo: ♩ = 96

Stand-ing in line, mark-ing time,___ wait-ing for the wel-fare dime.___

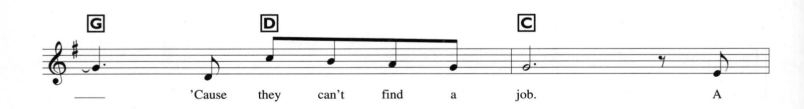

___ 'Cause they can't find a job. A

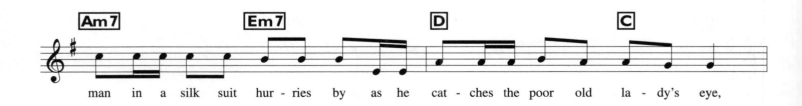

man in a silk suit hur-ries by as he cat-ches the poor old la-dy's eye,

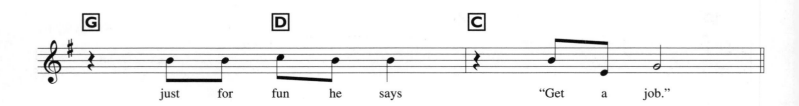

just for fun he says "Get a job."

THE WIND BENEATH MY WINGS

Words & Music by Jeff Silbar & Larry Henley
© Copyright House Of Gold Music Incorporated & Bobby Goldsboro Music Incorporated, USA.
Warner Chappell Music Limited, GrIffln House, 161 Hammersmlth Road, London W6.
All Rights Reserved. International Copyright Secured.

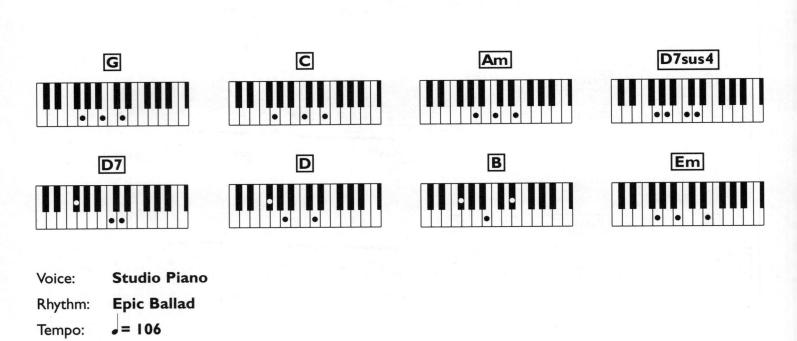

Voice: **Studio Piano**

Rhythm: **Epic Ballad**

Tempo: ♩ = 106

It must have been cold___ there___ in my sha - dow,

to nev - er have sun - light___ on your face.

You've been con - tent___ to let me shine,

you al - ways walked___ the step be - hind.___

WHO'S THAT GIRL?

Words & Music by A. Lennox & D. A. Stewart

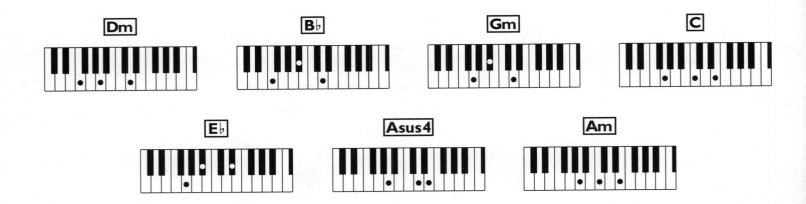

Voice: **Soprano Saxophone**

Rhythm: **Soul Ballad**

Tempo: ♩ = 122

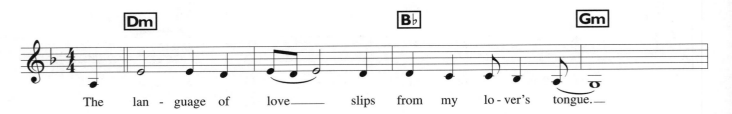

The lan - guage of love —— slips from my lo - ver's tongue. —

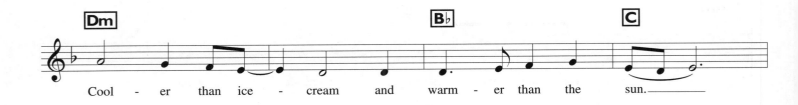

Cool - er than ice - cream and warm - er than the sun. —

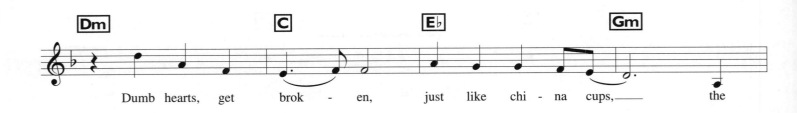

Dumb hearts, get brok - en, just like chi - na cups, —— the

lan - guage of love has left me bro - ken on the rocks. —— But there's

YOUNG AT HEART

Words & Music by Robert Hodgens, Siobhan Fahey, Keren Woodward & Sarah Dallin

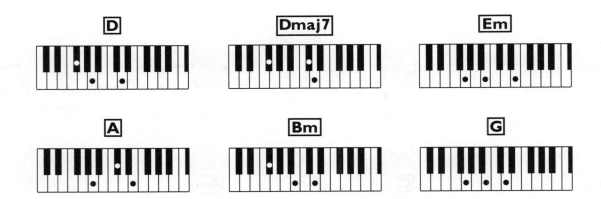

Voice: **Electric Piano 2**

Rhythm: **8 Beat Pop**

Tempo: ♩ = 124

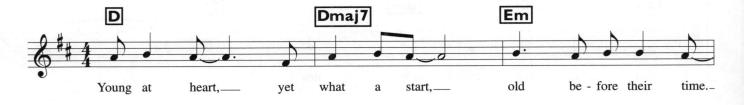

Young at heart,___ yet what a start,___ old be-fore their time.___

___ They mar-ried young___ for love at last___

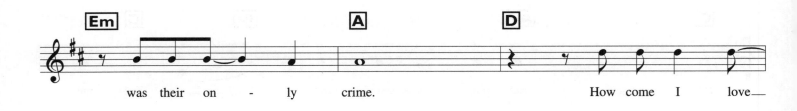

was their on - ly crime. How come I love___

___ them now,___ how come I love them more?

EASIEST KEYBOARD COLLECTION

Easy-to-play melody line arrangements for all keyboards with chord symbols and lyrics. Suggested registration, rhythm and tempo are included for each song together with keyboard diagrams showing left-hand chord voicings used.

 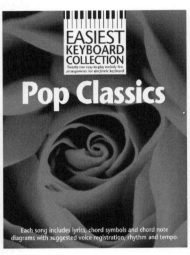  

Showstoppers

Consider Yourself (Oliver!), Do You Hear The People Sing? (Les Misérables), I Know Him So Well (Chess), Maria (West Side Story), Smoke Gets In Your Eyes (Roberta) and 17 more big stage hits.
Order No. AM944218

Pop Classics

A Whiter Shade Of Pale (Procol Harum), Bridge Over Troubled Water (Simon & Garfunkel), Crocodile Rock (Elton John) and 19 more classic hit songs, including Hey Jude (The Beatles), Imagine (John Lennon), and Massachusetts (The Bee Gees).
Order No. AM944196

90s Hits

Over 20 of the greatest hits of the 1990s, including Always (Bon Jovi), Fields Of Gold (Sting), Have I Told You Lately (Rod Stewart), One Sweet Day (Mariah Carey), Say You'll Be There (Spice Girls), and Wonderwall (Oasis).
Order No. AM944229

Abba

A great collection of 22 Abba hit songs. Includes: Dancing Queen, Fernando, I Have A Dream, Mamma Mia, Super Trouper, Take A Chance On Me, Thank You For The Music, The Winner Takes It All, and Waterloo.
Order No. AM959860

Also available...

Ballads, Order No. AM952116
The Beatles, Order No. NO90686
Boyzone, Order No. AM958331
Broadway, Order No. AM952127
Celine Dion, Order No. AM959850
Chart Hits, Order No. AM952083
Christmas, Order No. AM952105
Classic Blues, Order No. AM950697
Classics, Order No. AM952094

The Corrs, Order No. AM959849
Elton John, Order No. AM958320
Film Themes, Order No. AM952050
Hits of the 90s, Order No. AM955780
Jazz Classics, Order No. AM952061
Love Songs, Order No. AM950708
Pop Hits, Order No. AM952072
60s Hits, Order No. AM955768
80s Hits, Order No. AM955779

...plus many more!